This book belongs to
my friend:

_____

123

Math

Published by Scholastic Inc., 90 Old Sherman Turnpike, Danbury, CT 06816.

SCHOLASTIC and associated logos are trademarks and/or registered trademarks of Scholastic Inc.

ISBN 0-7172-6624-9

Printed in the U.S.A.

First Scholastic Printing, March 2007

A Birthday for Boots

by
Susan Hood

illustrated by
Susan Hall

SCHOLASTIC INC.

New York   Toronto   London   Auckland   Sydney
Mexico City   New Delhi   Hong Kong   Buenos Aires

One day, Dora planned a party for Boots.
She and her friends were all in cahoots.
Dora had saved up every last penny
To buy goody bags with Tico and Benny.

They started for home, pulling their wagon.
Backpack held the piñata—a colorful dragon.
They still had to decorate Dora's backyard,
Wrap all their presents, and sign Boots's card.

10 ten
diez

They rushed back home as fast as they could.
Someone was watching—and up to no good!

There were ten goody bags, all in a line.
But Swiper swooped in, and then there were . . .

9 nine
nueve

There were nine goody bags outside the gate.
But Swiper swiped one, and then there were . . .

8 eight
ocho

12

There were eight goody bags, when a race
car a-revvin'
Roared past the group, and then there were . . .

13

7 seven
siete

14

There were seven bags on the bridge made of bricks.
Swiper sailed up, and then there were . . .

6 six
seis

There were six bags, as they passed a beehive.
But Swiper buzzed by, and then there were . . .

5 five
cinco

There were five goody bags left from the store.
But Swiper popped up, and then there were . . .

4 four
cuatro

20

There were four bags underneath a tall tree.
Who grabbed one? You guessed it! Then there were . . .

3 three
tres

22

There were three goody bags—two red and one blue.
The sunflowers parted, and then there were . . .

23

There were two goody bags out in the sun.
An airplane flew by, and then there was . . .

There was one bag left when the cake was all done.
Until Swiper sneaked by, and then there was . . .

Then Boots arrived, and his friends yelled, "Surprise!"
But Dora just couldn't believe her own eyes.

"The goody bags are gone! Where did they go?
Swiper hid them, but where? Look! Do you know?"

"You did it! You found them. You found all ten!
On with the party!" yelled Dora, but then . . .
. . . Sneaky Swiper came back! He wasn't done yet.
There was one more thing that he wanted to get.

As he reached for the cake with bright yellow piping,
What did everyone yell?

He shrugged his shoulders. So much for his plan.
That fox snapped his fingers and hollered, "Oh, mannn!"

Nick Jr. Play-to-Learn™ Fundamentals
Skills every child needs, in stories every child will love!

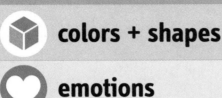 **colors + shapes**
Recognizing and identifying basic shapes and colors in the context of a story.

emotions
Learning to identify and understand a wide range of emotions, such as happy, sad, and excited.

imagination
Fostering creative thinking skills through role-play and make-believe.

math
Recognizing early math in the world around us, such as patterns, shapes, numbers, and sequences.

music + movement
Celebrating the sounds and rhythms of music and dance.

physical
Building coordination and confidence through physical activity and play.

problem solving
Using critical thinking skills, such as observing, listening, and following directions, to make predictions and solve problems.

reading + language
Developing a lifelong love of reading through high interest stories and characters.

science
Fostering curiosity and an interest in the natural world around us.

social skills + cultural diversity
Developing respect for others as unique, interesting people.

Math

Conversation Spark

Questions and activities for play-to-learn parenting.

There were lots of rhymes in this story. Can you think of two words that rhyme with the word *two*? How about three words that rhyme with *three*?

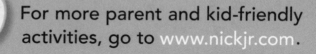

For more parent and kid-friendly activities, go to www.nickjr.com.

ENGLISH/SPANISH GLOSSARY and PRONUNCIATION GUIDE

English	Spanish	Pronunciation
Ten	Diez	dyehs
Nine	Nueve	NWEH-vay
Eight	Ocho	OH-choh
Seven	Siete	SYEH-tay
Six	Seis	seys
Five	Cinco	SIN-koh
Four	Cuatro	KWAH-troh
Three	Tres	trehs
Two	Dos	dohs
One	Uno	OO-noh
Happy Birthday	Feliz Cumpleaños	feh-LEES koom-play-AHN-yohs